Betsy Brown

Critical Thinking Activities

# Brain Teasers

## Grade 4

**Author:**

Carol Eichel


**Illustrator:**
Agi Palinay

**Editor:**
Dona Herweck Rice

**Editor-in-Chief:**
Sharon Coan, M.S. Ed.

**Editorial Project Manager:**
Evan D. Forbes, M.S. Ed.

**Art Director:**
Elayne Roberts

**Cover Artist:**
Keith Vasconcelles

**Imaging:**
Rick Chacón

**Production Manager:**
Phil Garcia





**Publishers:**
Rachelle Cracchiolo, M.S. Ed.
Mary Dupuy Smith, M.S. Ed.

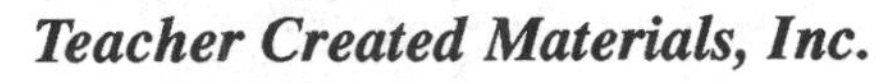


*Teacher Created Materials, Inc.*
P.O. Box 1040
Huntington Beach, CA 92647





Made in U.S.A.
ISBN-1-55734-489-2

# TABLE OF CONTENTS



# INTRODUCTION

*Brain Teasers* provides ways to exercise and develop brain power! Each page stands alone and can be used as a quick and easy filler activity. The pages can be distributed to students as individual worksheets or made into transparencies for presentation to the entire class at once. The book is divided into sections so the teacher can find activities related to a subject being taught or to a particular student's needs. The activities are especially useful in helping students develop:

- Logic and other critical thinking skills.
- Creative thinking skills.
- Research skills.
- Spelling skills.
- General vocabulary skills.

 

# FAMOUS PAIRS

Name the famous counterparts.

______________________ and Wilma Flintstone

______________________ and Wilbur Wright

______________________ and the Beaver

Calvin and ______________________

Roy Rogers and ______________________

Tom and ______________________

______________________ and Andy

______________________ and Jeff

______________________ and the Beast

Dick and ______________________

Desi and ______________________

Rocky and ______________________

______________________ and Hardy

______________________ and Daisy

______________________ and Jane

# PICK A PAIR

List as many items as you can that are sold in pairs. Can you think of at least 20?

1. ______________________________
2. ______________________________
3. ______________________________
4. ______________________________
5. ______________________________
6. ______________________________
7. ______________________________
8. ______________________________
9. ______________________________
10. ______________________________
11. ______________________________
12. ______________________________
13. ______________________________
14. ______________________________
15. ______________________________
16. ______________________________
17. ______________________________
18. ______________________________
19. ______________________________
20. ______________________________

Use the other side of the paper if you can come up with more than 20.

 

# THINGS WITH HOLES

Brainstorm a list of things with holes. Can you think of least 20?

1. ______________________
2. ______________________
3. ______________________
4. ______________________
5. ______________________
6. ______________________
7. ______________________
8. ______________________
9. ______________________
10. ______________________
11. ______________________
12. ______________________
13. ______________________
14. ______________________
15. ______________________
16. ______________________
17. ______________________
18. ______________________
19. ______________________
20. ______________________

Use the other side of the paper if you can come up with more than 20.

# NAME THREE OF EACH

Name three items that belong to each category.

1. Places animals live ______________________________
2. Things that are green ______________________________
3. Things with stripes ______________________________
4. Fairy tale characters ______________________________
5. Kinds of candy ______________________________
6. Mammals that live in the water ______________________________
7. Things in pairs ______________________________
8. Things you drink ______________________________
9. Things on your face ______________________________
10. Authors' names ______________________________
11. Things that float ______________________________
12. Shades of colors ______________________________
13. Things that give off light ______________________________
14. Places people live ______________________________
15. Provinces in Canada ______________________________

 

# ALL ALIKE

Read the words on each line. Explain how they are alike. An example has been done for you.

**North, South, East = cardinal directions**

1. Happy, Grumpy, Doc ________________________________
2. football, baseball, hockey________________________________
3. carnation, petunia, rose ________________________________
4. cougar, lion, panther________________________________
5. cake, ice cream, pie ________________________________
6. saw, hammer, screwdriver ________________________________
7. angry, sad, happy________________________________
8. dragons, unicorns, mermaids________________________________
9. hamburger, milk, butter ________________________________
10. alone, single, solo________________________________
11. orange, basketball, marble________________________________
12. bicycle, train, car ________________________________
13. corn, asparagus, squash ________________________________
14. Baby Ruth, Almond Joy, Snickers ________________________________
15. Carol, Cathy, Casie ________________________________

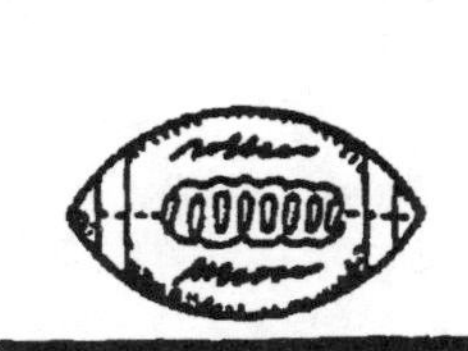

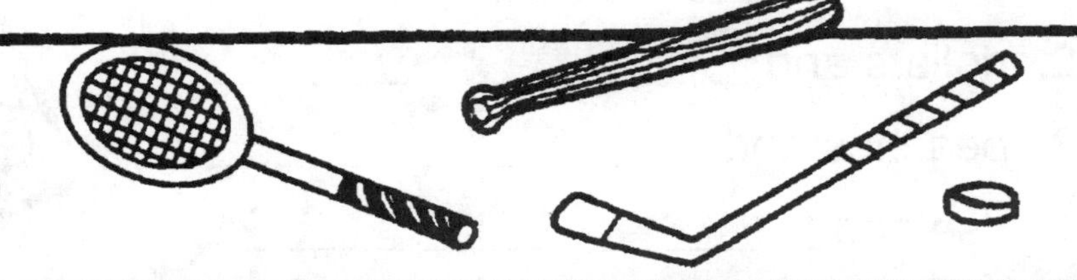

# WORD PAIRS

Write the missing half of each word pair.

1. huff and ____________________
2. tar and ____________________
3. law and ____________________
4. body and ____________________
5. nook and ____________________
6. mix and ____________________
7. satin and ____________________
8. cats and____________________
9. cream and____________________
10. black and ____________________
11. peace and____________________
12. scream and ____________________
13. back and ____________________
14. thick and ____________________
15. tooth and ____________________
16. sticks and ____________________
17. live and ____________________
18. lettuce and____________________
19. hammer and ____________________
20. prim and ____________________
21. fine and ____________________
22. dollars and____________________
23. peaches and ____________________
24. rise and ____________________

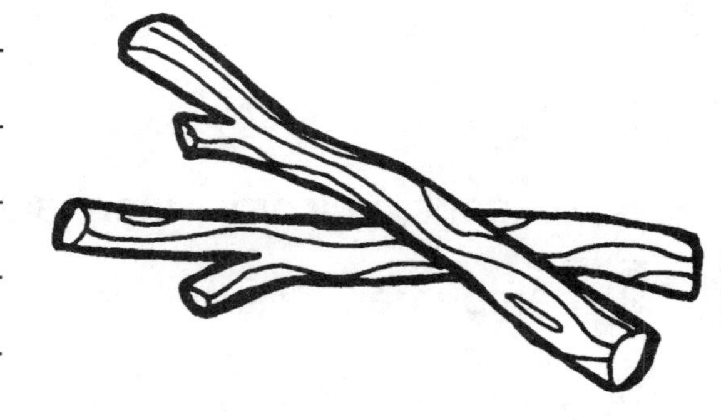

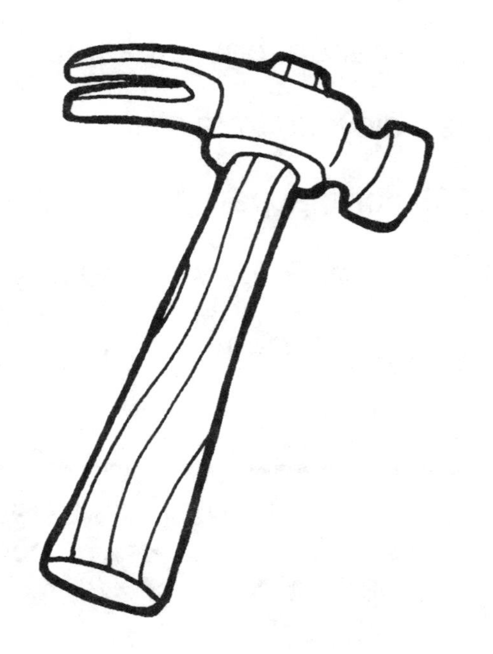

 

# WHICH ONE DOES NOT BELONG?

In each line below, one of the four words does not belong with the other three. Circle the one that does not fit. Explain what the others have in common. An example has been done for you.

**relish, hot dogs, mustard, ketchup = condiments**

1. Green, yellow, red, blue ____________
2. April, December, November, June ____________
3. Cirrus, calculus, cumulus, stratus ____________
4. Carrots, radishes, potatoes, cabbages ____________
5. Fork, comb, rake, shovel ____________
6. Chris, Carol, Susan, Cheryl ____________
7. Carnation, peony, tomato, rose ____________
8. Pie, cake, borwnie, candy bar ____________
9. Boy, lad, niece, man ____________
10. North America, Australia, Asia, Canada ____________
11. Dodgers, Cubs, Cowboys, Cardinals ____________
12. Orange, lemon, watermelon, grapefruit ____________
13. Laugh, giggle, chuckle, cry ____________
14. Duck, turkey, goose, pig ____________
15. Southeast, southwest, northeast, east ____________

# ELIZABETH

Mrs. Ginty has three girls in her ballet class who each go by a variation of the name Elizabeth. From the statements below, discover each girl's full name and age. Mark the correct boxes with an X.

1. Jones is younger than May but older than Smith.
2. Beth is not the youngest or the oldest.
3. Liz's last name is Smith.

| | **Jones** | **Smith** | **May** | **8** | **9** | **10** |
|---|---|---|---|---|---|---|
| **Bess** | | | | | | |
| **Liz** | | | | | | |
| **Beth** | | | | | | |

 

# GETTING FIT

David, Tom, Rick, and Roger have each found a way to keep fit. One jogs, one bikes, one golfs, and one swims. They each spend different amounts of time doing these activities. Using the clues below, determine each man's activity and the time he spends doing it. Mark the correct boxes with an X.

| | Jogging | Bicycling | Golf | Swimming | 15 | 30 | 45 | 60 |
|---|---|---|---|---|---|---|---|---|
| **David** | | | | | | | | |
| **Tom** | | | | | | | | |
| **Rick** | | | | | | | | |
| **Roger** | | | | | | | | |

1. Roger spends more time exercising than Tom or Rick, but he does not golf or bike.
2. David jogs.
3. Rick works out for 45 minutes.
4. Tom spends less time at his activity than the person who golfs, but he spends more time than David.

# A VISIT TO THE AMUSEMENT PARK

Katelyn, Kenny, Emily, and Howie recently visited their local amusement park to ride their favorite attractions—the roller coaster, the Ferris wheel, the carousel, and the bumper cars. While there, one ate a hamburger, another ate a corndog, another ate a hot dog, and the last ate bratwurst. Using the clues below, determine each person's favorite ride plus what each had to eat. Mark the correct boxes with an X.

| | roller coaster | Ferris wheel | carousel | bumper cars | hamburger | corndog | hot dog | bratwurst |
|---|---|---|---|---|---|---|---|---|
| **Katelyn** | | | | | | | | |
| **Kenny** | | | | | | | | |
| **Emily** | | | | | | | | |
| **Howie** | | | | | | | | |

1. The girls liked the roller coaster and bumper cars while the boys liked the Ferris wheel and the carousel.
2. Howie ate his food on a stick, while Katelyn ate hers on a hot dog bun.
3. Katelyn's favorite ride has hills.
4. The boy who loved the Ferris wheel also loves hot dogs.

 

# BIRTHDAY PARTIES

Eight children in one neighborhood will turn eleven this year. From the clues below, determine the month of each child's birthday. Mark the correct boxes with an X.

| | February 12 | August 25 | April 1 | July 14 | May 1 | January 1 | October 9 | March 10 |
|---|---|---|---|---|---|---|---|---|
| Sarah | | | | | | | | |
| Jill | | | | | | | | |
| Millie | | | | | | | | |
| Andrew | | | | | | | | |
| Max | | | | | | | | |
| Jeff | | | | | | | | |
| Andrea | | | | | | | | |
| Maeve | | | | | | | | |

1. Everyone celebrates on Jill's birthday.
2. Andrea's birthday is before Jeff's but after Millie's and Sarah's.
3. Sarah's birthday is exactly one month after Millie's.
4. Andrew's birthday is during the winter months.
5. Max's birthday comes after Andrea's but before Jeff's.

# FAVORITE TEAMS

Five boys root for five different baseball teams. Read the clues to determine which team each likes best. Mark the correct boxes with an X.

1. Will's bedroom is filled with posters and products from the A's.
2. Andrew's father is a big Cardinals fan, but Andrew is not.
3. Chad and Ryan like the Dodgers, the Reds, or the A's.
4. No boy's favorite team begins with the same letter as his name.

| | Cardinals | Dodgers | A's | Reds | White Sox |
|---|---|---|---|---|---|
| Chad | | | | | |
| Danny | | | | | |
| Andrew | | | | | |
| Ryan | | | | | |
| Will | | | | | |

# PALINDROMES

Palindromes are numbers, phrases, words, and sentences that read the same forward and backward. Examples are *mom* and *121*. See how many palindromes you can find in this puzzle. There are thirty-two.

| | | | | | | | | | | | | | | | | | | |
|---|---|---|---|---|---|---|---|---|---|---|---|---|---|---|---|---|---|---|
| S | C | O | M | L | K | B | B | U | Y | F | M | R | E | W | E | Q | T | F |
| L | D | P | A | A | C | O | I | D | F | N | U | N | T | R | H | N | H | U |
| E | O | I | E | C | B | Q | A | B | J | T | M | M | O | E | A | B | T | H |
| V | T | M | Y | E | P | D | K | P | K | N | L | T | A | O | N | H | I | O |
| E | O | O | J | X | P | M | G | M | O | R | I | Q | D | D | N | E | A | U |
| L | O | W | T | U | W | N | I | T | R | Q | M | Q | H | O | A | E | T | S |
| B | T | J | P | S | R | N | U | Y | Z | K | B | R | S | T | H | M | V | T |
| N | A | D | D | B | D | R | R | Z | P | L | J | O | O | U | Q | O | J | E |
| J | Z | S | O | Z | I | A | S | H | V | O | H | E | L | T | R | Z | O | O |
| D | E | E | D | M | G | D | B | A | Q | S | P | W | O | C | O | Z | X | T |
| X | Y | B | O | O | M | A | G | K | A | A | L | P | S | I | K | R | A | T |
| T | E | Q | B | M | R | R | G | W | D | G | Z | F | R | V | G | V | B | O |
| E | A | R | K | N | L | S | L | O | I | A | L | U | P | I | K | O | O | C |
| R | E | P | A | P | E | R | U | W | D | S | N | I | O | C | M | L | T | O |
| R | K | H | Y | O | X | P | R | M | J | N | E | N | T | E | R | K | G | G |
| E | O | J | A | F | O | I | U | X | K | P | M | B | A | C | E | B | I | S |
| T | H | A | K | D | J | N | N | X | R | G | G | E | Z | C | A | O | T | Q |
| S | E | E | S | U | Y | G | D | A | W | Z | P | B | H | A | B | D | T | W |
| W | L | S | R | D | S | S | P | J | A | V | E | S | C | P | F | N | M | G |

# SCHOOL DAYS

The word school appears 44 times in the word find below. Circle it each time you find it.

# GET TO KNOW YOUR CLASSMATES

Fill each blank with the name of a classmate who fits the description. Use each person's name only once. Do not forget to include yourself!

1. Lives or has lived on a farm ______________________
2. Has red hair ______________________
3. Has milked a cow ______________________
4. Has blue eyes ______________________
5. Has an unusual pet ______________________
6. Is left-handed ______________________
7. Was born outside the state ______________________
8. Has math as a favorite subject ______________________
9. Has been to a museum ______________________
10. Loves to camp ______________________
11. Has met a famous person ______________________
12. Has seen a rainbow ______________________
13. Has blue as a favorite color ______________________
14. Hates to eat liver ______________________
15. Has no cavities ______________________
16. Is an Elvis fan ______________________
17. Loves country music ______________________
18. Loves strawberry milkshakes ______________________
19. Has a middle name identical to yours ______________________
20. Has 7 as a favorite number ______________________

# WHAT'S THE QUESTION?

Write a question for each of the following answers.

1. ______________________________
   Genesis
2. ______________________________
   1848
3. ______________________________
   Amerigo Vespucci
4. ______________________________
   206
5. ______________________________
   Ludwig van Beethoven
6. ______________________________
   a hexagon
7. ______________________________
   Alaska
8. ______________________________
   88
9. ______________________________
   Yes
10. ______________________________
    Pluto
11. ______________________________
    A stethoscope
12. ______________________________
    The Statue of Liberty

 

# COMPLETE THE PHRASE

1. Blood, sweat, and ______________________________
2. Healthy, wealthy, and ______________________________
3. Morning, noon, and ______________________________
4. Men, women, and ______________________________
5. Faith, hope, and ______________________________
6. Readin', writin', and ______________________________
7. Hook, line, and ______________________________
8. Go, fight, ______________________________
9. Tall, dark, and ______________________________
10. Curly, Mo, and ______________________________
11. Coffee, tea, or ______________________________
12. Sun, moon, and ______________________________
13. Wynken, Blynken, and ______________________________
14. Eeny, meeny, miney, ______________________________
15. Rain, snow, sleet, and ______________________________

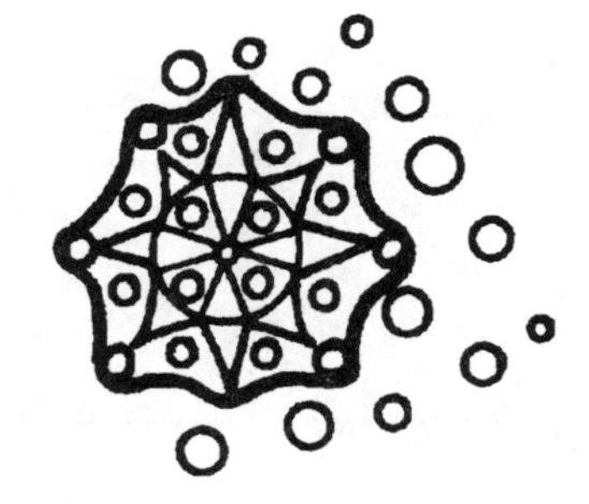

# HIDDEN MEANINGS

Explain the meaning of each box.

| | | |
|---|---|---|
| skating<br>thin ice | everyrightthing | MO*MAN*ON |
| 1. ______ | 2. ______ | 3. ______ |
| K<br>C<br>E<br>H<br>C | r<br>r o a d s<br>a<br>d<br>s | mind<br>———<br>matter |
| 4. ______ | 5. ______ | 6. ______ |
| I am/Myself | s<br>m<br>o<br>t<br>t<br>o<br>b | c<br>———<br>beneath |
| 7. ______ | 8. ______ | 9. ______ |
| hahandnd | N<br>W<br>O<br>T | H IJKLMN O |
| 10. ______ | 11. ______ | 12. ______ |

 

# MORE HIDDEN MEANINGS

Explain the meaning of each box.

1. ______________

HOUR

2. ______________

youJUSTme

3. ______________

POX

4. ______________

MAN
MOON

5. ______________

WORN

6. ______________

LONG
due

7. ______________

Loosen

8. ______________

theturkeystraw

9. ______________

G O
G N I
G O
G N I

10. ______________

me QUIT

11. ______________

SOTA

12. ______________

# HOW IS YOUR MEMORY?

Study the picture for three minutes. Then, put it out of sight. On another sheet of paper, list as many items from the picture as you can remember.

# AROUND YOUR HOUSE

Complete each expression with items found around your house. A word may be used more than once.

1. The mouse ran up the ________________________.
2. My ______________________________ runneth over.
3. The ______________________________ was bare.
4. The ____________________ ran away with the spoon.
5. Out of the ______________________ and into the fire
6. The butcher, the baker, the ________________ maker
7. Rub-a-dub-dub, three men in a __________________
8. ___________________________, mirror on the wall
9. Life is just a _______________________ of cherries.
10. Home on the ______________________________
11. Blue-_________________________________ special
12. Strike while the _________________________ is hot
13. Skeleton in the _____________________________

# LETTER ANSWERS

Use one or two letters of the alphabet to respond to each of the clues. The first one has been done for you.

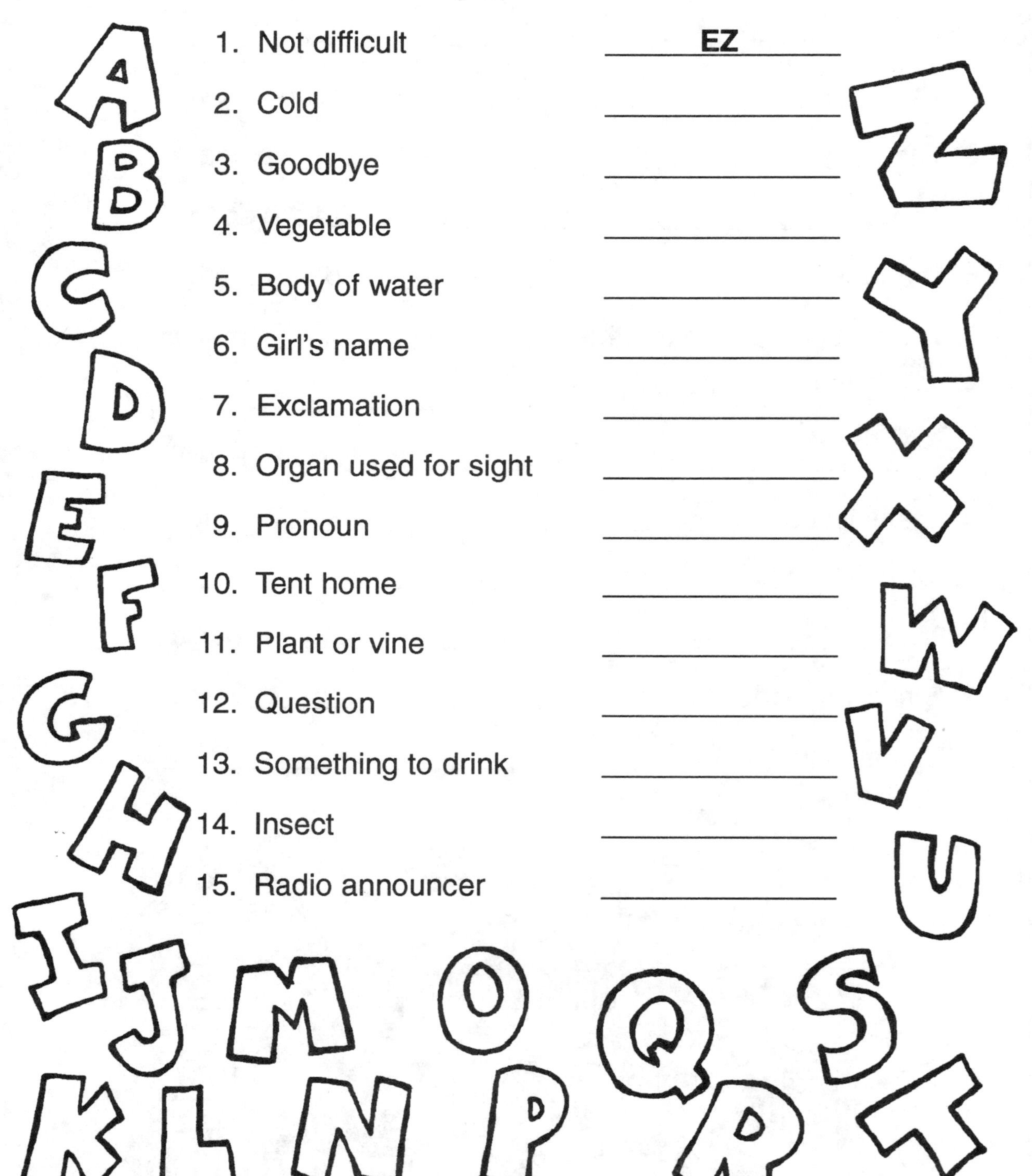

1. Not difficult ____EZ____
2. Cold ____________
3. Goodbye ____________
4. Vegetable ____________
5. Body of water ____________
6. Girl's name ____________
7. Exclamation ____________
8. Organ used for sight ____________
9. Pronoun ____________
10. Tent home ____________
11. Plant or vine ____________
12. Question ____________
13. Something to drink ____________
14. Insect ____________
15. Radio announcer ____________

 

# THREE AND FOUR OF A KIND

Complete each list.

1. Red, white, and ______________________________
2. Stop, look, and ______________________________
3. Sun, moon, and ______________________________
4. Readin', writin', and ______________________________
5. Ready, set, ______________________________
6. Red, yellow, and______________________________
7. Go, fight,______________________________
8. Stop, drop, and______________________________
9. Tall, dark, and______________________________
10. Rain, snow, sleet, and ______________________________
11. Larry, Mo, and ______________________________
12. Coffee, tea, or______________________________
13. Animal, vegetable, or ______________________________
14. Faith, hope, and ______________________________
15, Eeny, meeny, miney,______________________________

# SYMMETRY

Draw the other half of the figure, using the squares as a guide. Then, color the picture.

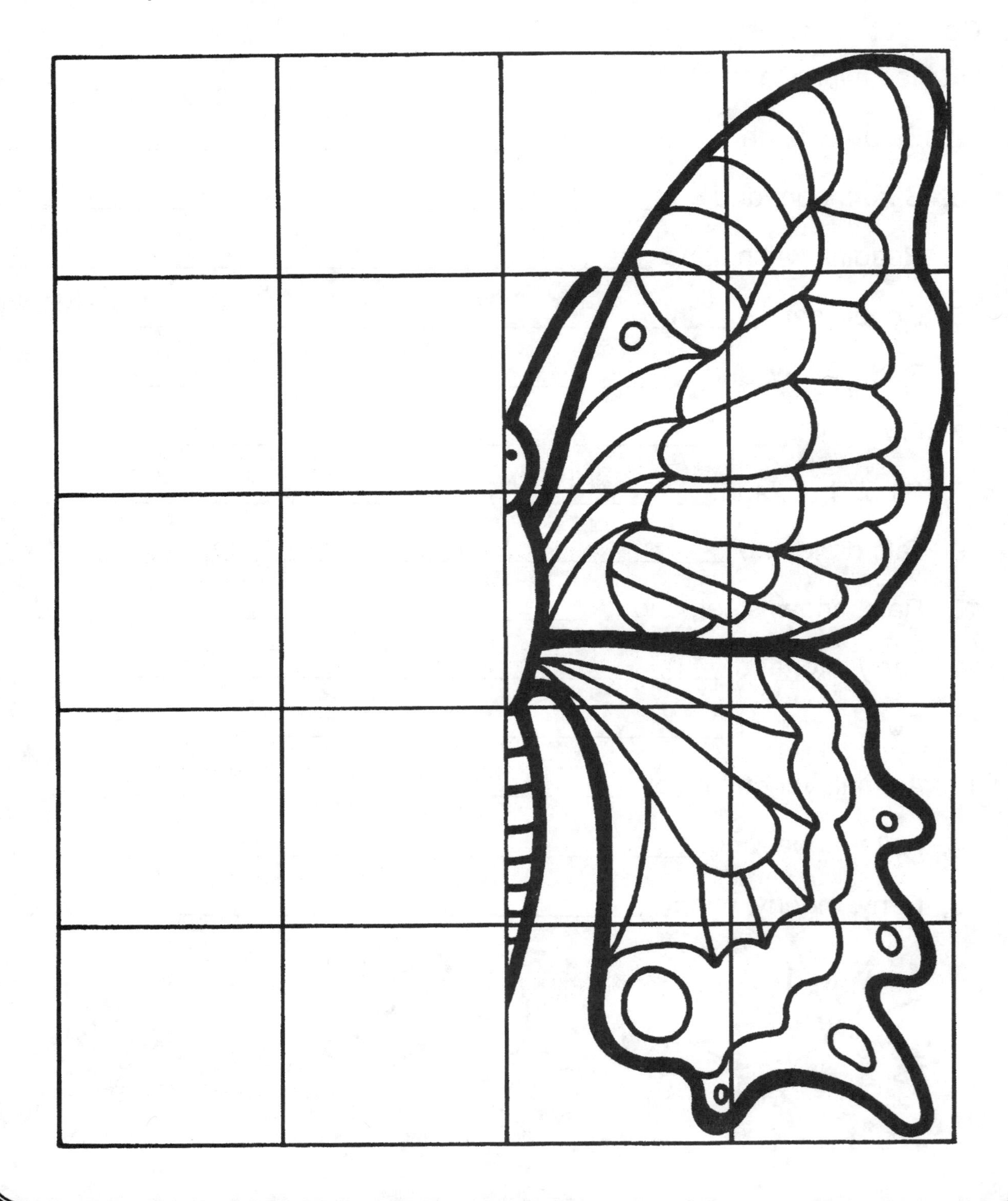

 

# ADDITION AND SUBTRACTION

Place + and - signs between the digits so that both sides of each equation are equal.

1. 6 4 1 2 6 2 = 15

2. 9 1 3 1 4 1 = 5

3. 9 3 4 1 2 3 = 14

4. 5 1 1 3 4 6 = 6

5. 9 8 6 3 5 3 = 8

6. 2 1 8 9 3 5 = 20

7. 5 3 2 4 1 5 = 12

8. 4 9 3 7 3 1 = 11

9. 7 6 2 8 7 1 = 3

10. 9 9 9 2 2 8 = 1

# NUMERAL-INITIAL EQUATIONS

Each equation below contains the initials of words that will make it complete. Find the missing words. An example has been done for you.

**9 = P in the SS** **planets in the solar system**

1. 4 = Q in a G ______
2. 100 = Y in a C ______
3. 6 = S of a H ______
4. 36 = I in a Y ______
5. 16 = O in a P ______
6. 88 = K on a P ______
7. 60 = M in an H ______
8. 366 = D in a LY ______
9. 3 = T in a T ______
10. 52 = C in a D ______
11. 206 = B in your B ______
12. 64 = S on a CB ______
13. 50 = S in the US ______
14. 13 = I in a BD ______
15. 2000 = P in a T ______
16. 1 = S in our SS ______
17. 5 = L in the GL ______
18. 5 = V in a Q ______
19. 9= P on a BT ______
20. 10 = MM in a CC ______

 

# WHAT'S THE MESSAGE?

Use the "phone code" (letters on the phone that correspond to numbers) to spell out words related to these famous people.

| | | |
|---|---|---|
| 1. Amelia Earhart | 284-2867 | ____________ |
| 2. Moses | 776-7438 | ____________ |
| 3. Beverly Cleary, Judy Blume | 288-4677 | ____________ |
| 4. Ted Kennedy | 736-2867 | ____________ |
| 5. George W. Carver | 732-6887 | ____________ |
| 6. Wright Brothers | 354-4487 | ____________ |
| 7. Milton Hershey | 226-3437 | ____________ |
| 8. Liberace | 742-6478 | ____________ |
| 9. Mike Piazza | 363-4377 | ____________ |
| 10. Franklin Roosevelt | 639-3325 | ____________ |
| 11. Helen Keller | 272-4553 | ____________ |
| 12. George Washington | 765-3437 | ____________ |
| 13. Norman Rockwell | 724-6837 | ____________ |
| 14. Kristi Yamaguchi | 752-8464 | ____________ |
| 15. Colin Powell | 436-3725 | ____________ |

# THE VALUE OF WORDS

In the Value Box, each letter of the alphabet has been given a dollar value. To find the value of a word, add the values of all the letters. For example, the word *school* is worth $72. (19 + 3 + 8 + 15 + 15 + 12 = 72) Write words with corresponding values in each of the boxes below.

**Value Box**

|  |  |
|---|---|
| A | = $1 |
| B | = $2 |
| C | = $3 |
| D | = $4 |
| E | = $5 |
| F | = $6 |
| G | = $7 |
| H | = $8 |
| I | = $9 |
| J | = $10 |
| K | = $11 |
| L | = $12 |
| M | = $13 |
| N | = $14 |
| O | = $15 |
| P | = $16 |
| Q | = $17 |
| R | = $18 |
| S | = $19 |
| T | = $20 |
| U | = $21 |
| V | = $22 |
| W | = $23 |
| X | = $24 |
| Y | = $25 |
| Z | = $26 |

**$10 Words**

**$20 Words**

**$50 Words**

**$100 Words**

**$101—$150 Words**

**$151—$200 Words**

 

# CHANGE FOR A DOLLAR

There are over 200 ways to make change for a dollar. Work with a friend to list as many ways as you can. List the coins in order on each line, from largest to smallest. (Hint: Working from large to small coins will help you find more ways to make change, too.) The list has been started for you. If you need more space, continue your list on the back of this paper.

Use the following abbreviations:

**hd** *(half dollar)* **q** *(quarter)* **d** *(dime)* **n** *(nickel)* **p** *(penny)*

1. 2hd ____________________
2. 1hd and 2q ____________
3. 1hd and 5d ____________
4. 1hd and 10n____________
5. ____________________
6. ____________________
7. ____________________
8. ____________________
9. ____________________
10. ____________________
11. ____________________
12. ____________________
13. ____________________
14. ____________________
15. ____________________
16. ____________________
17. ____________________
18. ____________________
19. ____________________
20. ____________________
21. ____________________
22. ____________________
23. ____________________
24. ____________________
25. ____________________
26. ____________________
27. ____________________
28. ____________________
29. ____________________
30. ____________________
31. ____________________
32. ____________________
33. ____________________
34. ____________________
35. ____________________
36. ____________________
37. ____________________
38. ____________________
39. ____________________
40. ____________________
41. ____________________
42. ____________________
43. ____________________
44. ____________________
45. ____________________
46. ____________________
47. ____________________
48. ____________________
49. ____________________
50. ____________________

# CHANGE, PLEASE

List the coins you would give each person below to make change for his or her dollar.

1. Dolly wants 1 coin for her $1.______________________________
2. Zac wants 6 coins for his $1. ______________________________
3. Holly wants 7 coins for her $1.____________________________
4. Andrew wants 10 coins for his $1. __________________________
5. Casie wants 15 coins for her $1. __________________________
6. Thomas wants 16 coins for his $1. ________________________
7. Chelsea wants 17 coins for her $1. ________________________
8. Austin wants 19 coins for his $1. __________________________
9. Marc wants 25 coins for his $1. ___________________________
10. Roberto wants 28 coins for his $1._________________________

# MATH TRIVIA

1. What do we call a chart that helps compare facts and numbers or quantities? ____________________
2. Does a right angle measure 60, 90, or 180 degrees? ____________
3. What do we call an area where people use the same clock time?

   ____________________________________________
4. What does "C" stand for in Roman numerals? ____________
5. What name is given to an 8-sided figure? ____________
6. How many millimeters are there in a centimeter? ____________
7. How many minutes are there in 2 hours? ____________
8. How many dots are there on a die? ____________
9. Will parallel lines intersect? ____________
10. How much is half of 20? ____________
11. How many zeros are there in a million? ____________
12. How do we find the area of a figure? ____________
13. Which number is a palindrome, 654 or 606? ____________
14. The number 66 carried to the nearest 10 is what number? ____________
15. How many degrees are there in a circle? ____________

# ENGLISH TRIVIA

1. What is a story you write about your own life called?

   ______________________________

2. Meg, Jo, Beth, and Amy are characters in what famous book?

   ______________________________

3. What is the name of the ancient Greek who wrote a group of fables?

   ______________________________

4. Who wrote *The Tale of Peter Rabbit?* ______________

5. What do we call a person who writes stories and books?

   ______________________________

6. What part of speech is used to modify verbs? ______________

7. What is Mark Twain's real name? ______________

8. What punctuation mark is placed at the end of a declarative sentence? ______________

9. What do we call words which are spelled the same forwards and backwards? ______________

10. In *Tales of a 4th Grade Nothing* who ate Peter's turtle?

    ______________________________

11. Which nouns are capitalized? ______________

12. In dialogue, what punctuation marks are put around the spoken words? ______________

13. What did the Brothers Grimm write? ______________

14. In a business letter, what punctuation mark is placed after the greeting? ______________

15. How many syllables are there in the word *catastrophe?* ______________

 

# SCIENCE TRIVIA

1. What do we call an instrument that makes small things look large? ______________________________
2. What is the largest planet in our solar system? ______________
3. What makes a skeleton move? ______________________
4. What is the hardest natural substance called? ______________
5. What device is used to measure air pressure? ______________
6. Which is larger, the moon or Earth? ____________________
7. For most people, what is the normal Farenheit body temperature? ______________________________
8. What is the Earth's path around the sun called? ______________
9. Which planet is farthest away from the sun? ______________
10. Which bones protect your lungs and heart? ______________
11. What name is given to the huge group of stars that are close together? ______________________
12. What is the colored part of the eye called? ______________
13. What is the term for the remains of things found in rock? __________
14. What kind of trees lose their leaves in autumn? ____________
15. What does the pulse measure? ______________________

# SOCIAL STUDIES TRIVIA

1. What is the capital of the United States' largest state? ____________
2. What is a piece of land with water on three sides called? ____________
3. How many white stripes are on the U.S. flag? ____________
4. Who assassinated President Lincoln? ____________
5. For whom is America named? ____________
6. Which Great Lake lies entirely in the U.S.? ____________
7. The Statue of Liberty is made of what metal? ____________
8. Who wrote *Poor Richard's Almanac?* ____________
9. When traveling north, what direction is to the left? ____________
10. What country gave the Statue of Liberty to the U.S.? ____________
11. In what city is the Liberty Bell located? ____________
12. Which two states are not within the continental U.S.? ____________
13. Who wrote *The Declaration of Independence*? ____________
14. What American landmark stands on Liberty Island? ____________
15. Who is said to have made the U.S. flag? ____________

# GENERAL TRIVIA

1. What is another name for a moving staircase? ________________
2. How often does leap year occur? ________________
3. Most fairy tales begin with what four words? ________________
4. What are five babies born to the same mother at the same time called? ________________
5. What do we call a stand with three legs? ________________
6. What does a philatelist collect? ________________
7. What do you do with a piñata? ________________
8. What color is ebony? ________________
9. What is a group of lions called? ________________
10. What is the left side of a ship called? ________________
11. What type of hat is Abraham Lincoln famous for wearing? ________________
12. Who lives in Aladdin's lamp? ________________
13. What do we call the water-filled ditch around a castle? ________________
14. What is the hole in a sewing needle called? ________________
15. What animal's foot is said to be a good luck charm? ________________

# TRUE OR FALSE

Read each of the following statements carefully. Which of the statements are true and which are false? Be prepared to defend your answer.

1. ________ The signal SOS means save our ship.
2. ________ Of the five Great Lakes, only Lake Superior lies entirely within the U.S.
3. ________ Every insect has six legs.
4. ________ Los Angeles is the capital of California.
5. ________ All prime numbers are odd numbers.
6. ________ The diamond is the hardest of all minerals.
7. ________ Numismatics is the science of numbers.
8. ________ A ladybird is a female bird.
9. ________ The Lincoln Memorial appears on the back of the American five-dollar bill.
10. ________ Arbor Day is celebrated on the same day around the world.
11. ________ The air we breathe is mostly nitrogen.
12. ________ Only four months of the year have thirty days.
13. ________ The longest river in the world is the Nile.
14. ________ In a lunar eclipse, the moon is between the earth and the sun.
15. ________ A firefly is a type of fly.

 

# HOW MANY?

Answer each question with a number.

How many . . .

1. . . . sides in a dodecagon? ______________________
2. . . . books in the Bible? ______________________
3. . . . sheets in a quire? ______________________
4. . . . people aboard the *Mayflower?* ______________________
5. . . . rooms in the White House? ______________________
6. . . . items in a baker's dozen? ______________________
7. . . . rings on the Olympic flag? ______________________
8. . . . instruments in a quartet? ______________________
9. . . . bones in the human body? ______________________
10. . . . adult teeth in the mouth? ______________________
11. . . . keys on a piano? ______________________
12. . . . items in a gross? ______________________
13. . . . original colonies in the United States? ______________________
14. . . . years in a century? ______________________
15. . . . wheels on a unicycle? ______________________

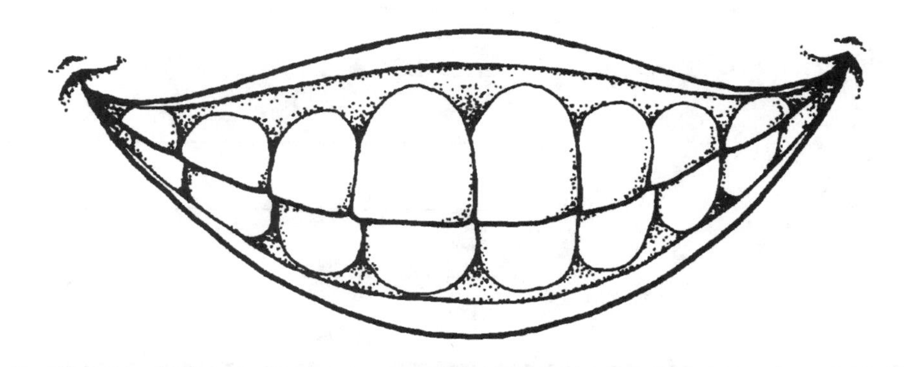

# RHYMING WORD PAIRS

Find an adjective that rhymes with a noun so that together, the two words have about the same meaning as the phrase that is given. An example has been done for you.

**soaked dog = soggy doggy**

1. skinny horse ______________________
2. unhappy friend ______________________
3. smooth hen ______________________
4. dog with a license ______________________
5. burned bread ______________________
6. purple gorilla ______________________
7. downcast father ______________________
8. comical rabbit ______________________
9. girl from Switzerland ______________________
10. beetle embrace ______________________
11. crude man ______________________
12. car crash ______________________
13. dog kiss ______________________
14. overweight feline ______________________
15. adorable bird ______________________
16. bashful man ______________________
17. home for a rodent ______________________
18. large swine ______________________
19. happy boy ______________________
20. loafing flower ______________________

 

# ABBREVIATIONS

Write the meaning of each abbreviation.

1. Pres. ____________________
2. ASAP ____________________
3. Adj. ____________________
4. Lbs. ____________________
5. Max. ____________________
6. Etc. ____________________
7. Sept. ____________________
8. M.A. ____________________
9. I.O.U. ____________________
10. B.C. ____________________
11. C.O.D. ____________________
12. R.S.V.P. ____________________
13. S.A.S.E. ____________________
14. S.A. ____________________
15. Bldg. ____________________
16. RR ____________________
17. Prep. ____________________
18. Hdqrs. ____________________
19. D.A. ____________________
20. D.S.T. ____________________

# ACROSTICS

Acrostics are word puzzles or poems in which the first or last letters of each line form a word or words. The first letters of each line below form the words *recess* and *friends.* Complete the acrostics by writing a phrase or sentence on each line that begins with the letter given and relates to the subjects "recess" or "friends."

**R** ______________________________

**E** ______________________________

**C** ______________________________

**E** ______________________________

**S** ______________________________

**S** ______________________________

**F** ______________________________

**R** ______________________________

**I** ______________________________

**E** ______________________________

**N** ______________________________

**D** ______________________________

**S** ______________________________

# COMPETITIVE WORD CHAIN

Two or more players begin at the same time to fill in all the blanks with a 3-, 4-, 5-, or 6-letter word, depending on the number of blanks given. Each word must begin with the last letter of the preceding word. The first word may start with any letter. (Words may not be repeated.) The first player to complete all the words wins.

1. _____ _____ _____
2. _____ _____ _____ _____
3. _____ _____ _____ _____ _____
4. _____ _____ _____ _____
5. _____ _____ _____
6. _____ _____ _____ _____
7. _____ _____ _____ _____ _____
8. _____ _____ _____ _____
9. _____ _____ _____
10. _____ _____ _____ _____
11. _____ _____ _____ _____ _____
12. _____ _____ _____ _____
13. _____ _____ _____
14. _____ _____ _____ _____
15. _____ _____ _____ _____ _____
16. _____ _____ _____ _____
17. _____ _____ _____
18. _____ _____ _____ _____
19. _____ _____ _____ _____ _____
20. _____ _____ _____ _____
21. _____ _____ _____

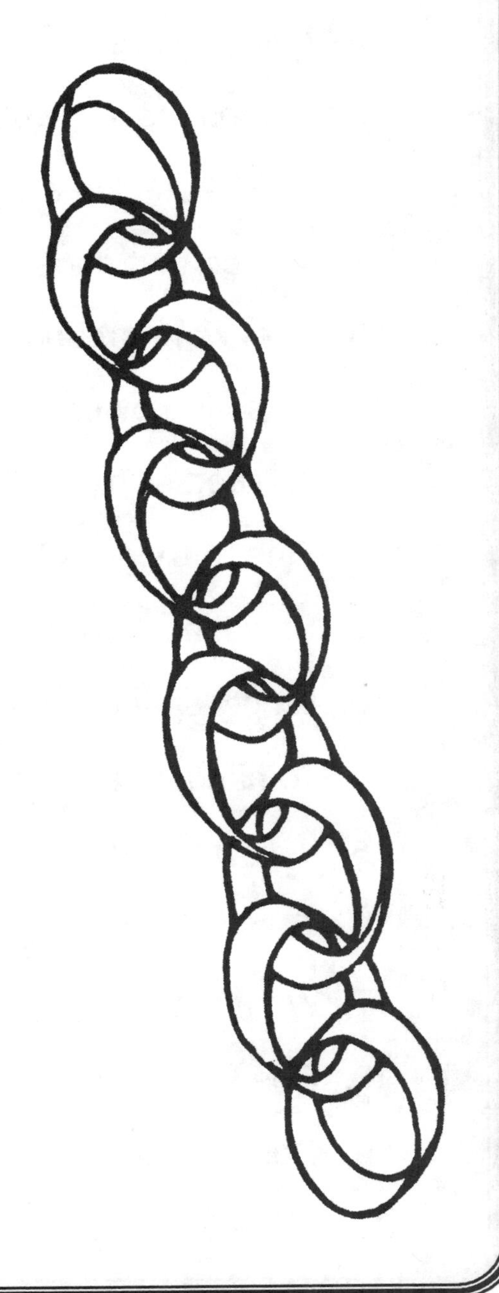

# WORD WINDERS

Use the clues to help you fill in the blanks and circles. Only the circled letters change from one word to the next.

1. Antonym for hot — c o l d
2. Pony — ___ ___ ___ ○
3. Stroke of lightning — ○ ___ ___ ___
4. Courageous — ___ ___ ___ ○
5. Without hair — ___ ○ ___ ___
6. Object used in a soccer game — ___ ___ ___ ○
7. Device that rings — ___ ○ ___ ___
8. Item worn around the waist — ___ ___ ___ ○
9. To soften by using heat — ○ ___ ___ ___
10. To shed skin — ___ ○ ___ ___
11. Fine, furry growth of fungi — ___ ___ ___ ○
12. Small, burrowing animal — ___ ___ ___ ○
13. Empty space — ○ ___ ___ ___
14. To hang on to something — ___ ___ ___ ○
15. Yellow metallic element — ○ ___ ___ ___
16. To bend and crease — ○ ___ ___ ___
17. What you eat — ___ ___ ○ ___
18. One who lacks good sense — ___ ___ ___ ○
19. Object used to do work — ○ ___ ___ ___
20. Place to swim — ○ ___ ___ ___

 

# WORD CHAIN

Use the last two letters of the first word in the word chain to begin the next word. Continue throughout the chain. The first one has been done for you.

1. Sprouted ______grew______
2. Female sheep ____________
3. Undesirable in the garden ____________
4. Able to be eaten ____________
5. Character of the alphabet ____________
6. To rub out ____________
7. Division of the year ____________
8. One time ____________
9. To observe some special occasion ____________
10. Message transmitted by telegraph ____________
11. Italian word for love ____________
12. To see what words on a page mean ____________
13. To allow to enter ____________
14. Skin irritation ____________
15. Type of fowl ____________
16. To amuse ____________

# WORD-STAIR PUZZLE

Use the clues below to fill in this grid.

1. 5 x 2 = ____________
2. used to catch butterflies
3. story
4. separately considered
5. rabbit

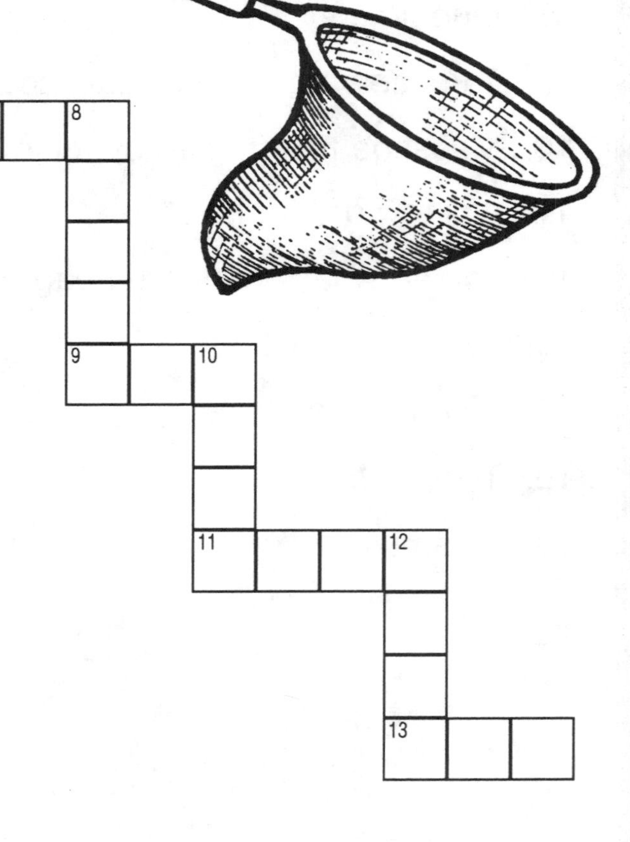

6. third planet from the sun
7. grasp
8. happening each day
9. sí
10. to move through the water
11. letters
12. strong liking
13. one of the sense organs

 

# BAR NONE

Each phrase below is a clue for a word that contains the word BAR.

1. Backyard cookout__________
2. Building for lodging soldiers __________
3. Weight-lifting equipment__________
4. Uncivilzed person__________
5. Farm building __________
6. Type of shrub __________
7. Founder of the American Red Cross __________
8. Sale-priced item __________
9. Deep voice __________
10. Baron's wife __________
11. Popular doll __________
12. River vessel __________
13. Predatory fish __________
14. Riding without a saddle __________
15. City in Spain__________

# COLD AS ICE

Each phrase below is a clue for a word or phrase that contains the word ICE.

1. 200th birthday________________
2. The cost of ________________
3. Sliver or piece________________
4. Rodents ________________
5. Large mass of ice floating in the sea ________________
6. Black or red candy ________________
7. Flavoring or seasoning________________
8. Country on an island in the North Atlantic ________________
9. Grain________________
10. Dinosaur________________
11. Second in commmand ________________
12. Lewis Carroll book ________________
13. Suggestion about what should be done________________
14. Room in which to conduct business________________
15. Liquid part of fruits ________________
16. Large muscles in the upper arms________________
17. Gadget ________________
18. Attract or tempt________________
19. Persons whose duty is keeping order ________________
20. Cut into small cubes________________
21. Of fine quality ________________
22. Observe ________________
23. Three times ________________
24. Small, wingless, parasitic insect________________
25. Long-running television game show________________

 

# THE MIDAS TOUCH

Each phrase below is a clue for a word or phrase that contains the word GOLD.

1. James Bond movie ____________________
2. Small orange-colored fish ____________________
3. To avoid work ____________________
4. Ghana ____________________
5. Young girl in *The Three Bears* ____________________
6. Person who extracts money or gifts by coaxing or flattery __________
7. Gold in very small bits or powder ____________________
8. Bright yellow ____________________
9. Wild duck ____________________
10. Principle to live by ____________________
11. Site where gold is obtained ____________________
12. Event of 1848 ____________________
13. 50 years after a wedding ____________________
14. Gold held by the central bank ____________________
15. Fall plant with tall stalks ____________________
16. Person who makes articles of gold ____________________
17. Small yellow songbird ____________________

# ALL THUMBS

Each phrase below is a clue for a word or phrase that contains the word THUMB.

1. Gardener's gift ______________________________
2. Barnum and Bailey attraction ______________________________
3. Go-ahead sign ______________________________
4. Tiny fairy tale character ______________________________
5. Impression made by underside of the thumb ______________________________
6. Hitchhike ______________________________
7. Signal of disapproval ______________________________
8. To search the pages of a book ______________________________
9. Push pin ______________________________
10. Guideline ______________________________
11. Clumsy in handling something ______________________________
12. Completely dominated by someone ______________________________
13. Treat or regard with disdain ______________________________

# GO TEAM GO

Each phrase below is a clue for a word or phrase that contains the word GO.

1. Animal ____________________
2. Sport ____________________
3. Water taxi ____________________
4. Valuable mineral ____________________
5. Past tense of go ____________________
6. Guiding principle ____________________
7. Type of dog ____________________
8. End or aim ____________________
9. Another name for a peanut ____________________
10. Intermediary ____________________
11. To eat hurriedly ____________________
12. Mischievous or scary elf ____________________
13. Beautiful ____________________
14. Ape ____________________
15. Stew ____________________
16. To annoy or irritate ____________________
17. Drinking glass with a stem ____________________
18. Spectacles used to protect the eyes ____________________
19. Movie and book title about the old South ____________________
20. Giant in the Bible ____________________
21. Loose, flowing garment ____________________
22. Fruit ____________________
23. Dance ____________________
24. Fruit of a trailing or climbing plant ____________________
25. Type of bird ____________________

# HIDDEN ANIMALS

Hidden in each sentence is the name of an animal. Each can be found either in the middle of a word or by combining the end of one word with the beginning of the next. Underline the animal name in each sentence. An example has been done for you.

Mar**c ow**ns a sporting goods store. **(cow)**

1. We will leave for the picnic at 11:45. ______________________
2. To and fro goes the pendulum. ______________________
3. I can go at 7:30. ______________________
4. “Ski down the beginner’s slope,” said the instructor. ______________________
5. They do good work. ______________________
6. He can’t stand to be around cigarette smoke. ______________________
7. Susan came late to the party. ______________________
8. Is Mr. Roy Stern the new principal? ______________________
9. The teacher made Ernie stay after school. ______________________
10. Magnus ate a whole bowl of popcorn while watching the movie.

    ______________________
11. Noah entered the ark with his family. ______________________
12. Sheryl, I only have 50 cents in my pocket. ______________________
13. Steffi should be pleased with the results. ______________________
14. Please allow me to help you. ______________________
15. Try some of these green grapes. ______________________

 

# DOUBLE ANYONE

Use the following clues to find words that contain consecutive double letters.

1. An animal ____________________
2. One of the four seasons____________________
3. Sport played in the fall ____________________
4. High level of understanding ____________________
5. To draw aimlessly____________________
6. Pirate ____________________
7. Winged insect____________________
8. Animal with a long neck ____________________
9. Person who asks for handouts____________________
10. Earth's natural satellite____________________
11. Seasoning____________________
12. Flock of geese ____________________
13. Move from side to side____________________
14. To take for a period of time ____________________
15. Grief, sadness ____________________
16. Poem of fourteen lines____________________
17. Paper used in secret voting ____________________
18. Great work of literature____________________

# WHAT DOES IT MEAN?

Match each definition with a word or phrase from the word bank.

1. An international code signal of distress ____________________
2. Appetizer ____________________
3. A left-handed person ____________________
4. Awesome ____________________
5. Able to use either hand equally well ____________________
6. A sack for left-overs ____________________
7. A useless item ____________________
8. To speak without preparation ____________________
9. Wordy, pompous language____________________
10. The other way around ____________________
11. *Gracias* ____________________
12. Served with ice cream on top____________________
13. Oodles ____________________
14. Magic ____________________
15. “And the rest” ____________________

**Word Bank**

| | |
|---|---|
| ad lib | white elephant |
| SOS | et cetera |
| gobbledy gook | hors d'oeuvre |
| vice versa | doggy bag |
| hodgepodge | great |
| southpaw | pet peeve |
| thank you | ambidextrous |
| many | hocus-pocus |
| á la mode | |

 

# DECODE U.S. STATES AND INVENTORS

Each group of letters below is a list of related words in code. Each group has its own code. Brainstorm some words to fit each category. Once you have identified a word, use the known letters to decode the other words.

**U.S. States**

1. BQA HQIDRC ______
2. FCGJN OPSCJP ______
3. BCEJN RPECTDBP ______
4. BQA VQEFQK ______
5. BQA NPHLFNDEQ ______
6. ENCOQ DFTPBO ______
7. FCGJN RPECTDBP ______
8. BQA KCES ______
9. AQFJ MDEUDBDP ______
10. BCEJN OPSCJP ______

**Inventors**

1. NFRAMYKA ______
2. NEYHDA ______
3. SRBHTRA ______
4. VEHSAPSFV ______
5. TRFXDAK ______
6. IWKHASG ______
7. WDIS ______
8. PSYY ______
9. SOKBDA ______
10. VDDOGSRF ______

# DECODE MATH AND SCHOOL TERMS

Each group of letters below is a list of related words in code. Each group has its own code. Brainstorm some words to fit each category. Once you have identified a word, use the known letters to decode the other words.

**Math Terms**

1. RPPGHGDO ______________________________
2. IJMHGAMGQRHGDO ______________________________
3. AFDPJQH ______________________________
4. PGCGKGDO ______________________________
5. WBJRHGDO ______________________________
6. WBJGCRMWOH ______________________________
7. PGRIWHWF ______________________________
8. PFWR ______________________________
9. AFDTRTGMGHE ______________________________
10. KBJRFW FDDH ______________________________

**School Terms**

1. ATWTGG ______________________________
2. RPBG ______________________________
3. KTGHG ______________________________
4. PFRPJPW ______________________________
5. SCCHG ______________________________
6. ADFTA ______________________________
7. WCRBPGG ______________________________
8. ELPWKLA ______________________________
9. BTJWNFG ______________________________

 

# THOSE FAMOUS THREES

Sometimes a certain number brings to mind a character in a story, rhyme, or phrase. Name the famous 3's below, either by their names or situations..

1. The three wise men ______________________________
2. The three little pigs ______________________________
3. The three blind mice ______________________________
4. The three bears ______________________________
5. The three wise monkeys ______________________________
6. The three R's ______________________________
7. The three Stooges ______________________________
8. The three Musketeers ______________________________
10. The three gifts from the wise men ______________________________
11. Donald Duck's three nephews ______________________________
14. The three dimensions (3-D) ______________________________

# ALL FIVE VOWELS

Make a list of words that have all five vowels within them.

 

# SUMMERTIME

List words related to summertime that begin with each letter of the alphabet.

A ____________________

B ____________________

C ____________________

D ____________________

E ____________________

F ____________________

G ____________________

H ____________________

I ____________________

J ____________________

K ____________________

L ____________________

M ____________________

N ____________________

O ____________________

P ____________________

Q ____________________

R ____________________

S ____________________

T ____________________

U ____________________

V ____________________

W ____________________

X ____________________

Y ____________________

Z ____________________

# TWO OF A KIND

Make a list of words that contain two of one letter of the alphabet. Examples include *aardvark, baby, cartoon,* and *dawdle.*

 

# FROM A TO Z

List as many words as you can that begin and end with the letters of the alphabet that are listed.

A ______________________________ Z
B ______________________________ Y
C ______________________________ X
D ______________________________ W
E ______________________________ V
F ______________________________ U
G ______________________________ T
H ______________________________ S
I ______________________________ R
J ______________________________ Q
K ______________________________ P
L ______________________________ O
M ______________________________ N
N ______________________________ M
O ______________________________ L
P ______________________________ K
Q ______________________________ J
R ______________________________ I
S ______________________________ H
T ______________________________ G
U ______________________________ F
V ______________________________ E
W ______________________________ D
X ______________________________ C
Y ______________________________ B
Z ______________________________ A

# WHAT'S TO EAT?

List food items that begin with each letter of the alphabet.

A ______________________________

B ______________________________

C ______________________________

D ______________________________

E ______________________________

F ______________________________

G ______________________________

H ______________________________

I ______________________________

J ______________________________

K ______________________________

L ______________________________

M ______________________________

N ______________________________

O ______________________________

P ______________________________

Q ______________________________

R ______________________________

S ______________________________

T ______________________________

U ______________________________

V ______________________________

W ______________________________

X ______________________________

Y ______________________________

Z ______________________________

 

# EDUCATION

List all the words you can make from the letters in education. (Note: All the words in your list must have at least 3 letters, and each letter can be used only once in each word.)

# ARAB TO ZEBRA

Write a word that begins with "A" and ends with "B." Continue through the alphabet. Finish with a word that begins with "Z" and ends with "A." The list has been started for you. (**Note:** You may not find a word for every letter combination.)

Arab

basic

cold

d ________________ e

e ________________ f

f ________________ g

g ________________ h

h ________________ i

i ________________ j

j ________________ k

k ________________ l

l ________________ m

m ________________ n

n ________________ o

o ________________ p

p ________________ q

q ________________ r

r ________________ s

s ________________ t

t ________________ u

u ________________ v

v ________________ w

w ________________ x

x ________________ y

y ________________ z

z ________________ a

 

# CODED MESSAGE

Answer each question below. Then use the code to reveal a famous proverb.

1. If 9 x 9 = 81, circle L. If it does not, circle U.
2. If the Atlantic Ocean is west of Canada, circle V. If it is east of Canada, circle Y.
3. If lavender is a shade of purple, circle D. If it is not, circle M.
4. If Hawaii is an island, circle W. If it is a peninsula, circle K.
5. If homophones are words that mean the opposite, circle L. If they are not, circle T.
6. If the Statue of Liberty was given to the United States by Canada, circle B. If it was not, circle F.
7. If a telescope is used to view things that are far away, circle R. If it is not, circle P.
8. If Robert E. Lee was a Confederate general, circle A. If he was a Union general, circle I.
9. If Alberta is a state in the U.S., circle O. If it is a province in Canada, circle E.
10. If 6 x 8 + 2 is equal to 10 x 5, circle S. If it is not, circle R.
11. If America was named after Christopher Columbus, circle O. If it was named after Amerigo Vespucci, circle N.
12. If southpaws are people who write left-handed, circle K. If they write right-handed, circle S.
13. If an octagon has five sides, circle E. If it has eight sides, circle O.
14. If Ronald Reagan was once a movie star, circle H. If he was not, circle L.
15. If IX means 11 in Roman numerals, circle J. If it means 9, circle C.

___ ___   ___ ___ ___ ___ ___ ___
8 11   8 6 6 1 9 8

___ ___ ___   ___ ___ ___ ___ ___   ___ ___ ___
3 8 2   12 9 9 6 10   5 14 9

___ ___ ___ ___ ___ ___   ___ ___ ___ ___.
3 13 15 5 13 7   8 4 8 2

# BEGINNING AND END

Each of the following clues has an answer in which the first letter is the same as the last letter.

1. Loss of memory ______
2. The fireplace floor ______
3. A type of bird ______
4. A type of boat ______
5. A province in Canada ______
6. Opposite of minimum ______
7. A continent ______
8. The act or words of welcoming someone ______
9. To regain health after an illness ______
10. The most abundant gas in the atmosphere ______
11. To roll about ______
12. Having made twice as much ______
13. To rub out ______
14. A gas used in lighted signs ______

# COMPOUND WORDS

Choose a word from column A or B and combine it with a word from column C or D to make a compound word. Some words will go together in more than one combination, but there is only one combination that will use all words.

| A | B | C | D |
|---|---|---|---|
| any- | south- | -road | -ball |
| school- | back- | -ever | -board |
| sea- | snow- | -shore | -east |
| grand- | who- | -day | -paper |
| home- | head- | -made | -where |
| under- | cow- | -doors | -boy |
| every- | news- | -one | -bone |
| black- | bed- | -room | -stand |
| rail- | after- | -father | -time |
| else- | out- | -noon | -line |

| | | | |
|---|---|---|---|
| ____________ | ____________ | ____________ | ____________ |
| ____________ | ____________ | ____________ | ____________ |
| ____________ | ____________ | ____________ | ____________ |
| ____________ | ____________ | ____________ | ____________ |
| ____________ | ____________ | ____________ | ____________ |

# COMPLETE THE PHRASE

Complete the following phrases with the first things that come to mind. There are no incorrect responses to this activity.

1. What I want most in the world is
___
2. I feel sorry for
___
3. When someone hurts me, I
___
4. If I was 21, I
___
5. I like to eat at
___
6. I am really good at
___
7. I never want to forget
___
8. Sometimes I dream about
___
9. When I was little
___
10. My favorite time of day is
___
11. I wish I could
___
12. I would rather read than
___
13. I do not like to
___
14. I love it when
___
15. I am afraid of
___

 

# ANTONYMS, SYNONYMS, AND HOMOPHONES

List whether each pair of words is made of antonyms (A), synonyms (S), or homophones (H).

1. Maximum/minimum ____________________
2. Recall/remember ____________________
3. Allow/forbid ____________________
4. Chili/chilly ____________________
5. Often/frequently ____________________
6. Coarse/course ____________________
7. Birth/berth ____________________
8. Honest/sincere ____________________
9. Appear/vanish ____________________
10. Liberty/freedom ____________________
11. Gate/gait ____________________
12. Bright/dull ____________________
13. Easy/simple ____________________
14. Foreword/forward ____________________
15. Guessed/guest ____________________
16. Common/rare ____________________
17. Clear/plain ____________________
18. Herd/heard ____________________
19. Aid/assist ____________________
20. Defeat/victory ____________________

# PALINDROMES

Palindromes are words, phrases, sentences, or numbers that read the same forward and backward. Write a palindrome that relates to each word or phrase below. An example has been done for you.

**small dog = pup**

1. Man's name ______________________
2. Past tense of the verb do ______________________
3. Relating to government or citizenship ______________________
4. 12:00 o'clock ______________________
5. Woman in a convent ______________________
6. Female sheep ______________________
7. A flower ______________________
8. Little chick's noise ______________________
9. Ancient king ______________________
10. Eskimo canoe ______________________
11. Small child ______________________
12. Woman's name ______________________
13. Flat, even ______________________
14. Trick or joke ______________________
15. Songs sung alone ______________________

# PROVERBS

Proverbs are old, familiar sayings that often give advice for daily living. Complete each of the following proverbs.

1. Never put off until tomorrow . . .
   ______________________________
2. A friend in need . . .
   ______________________________
3. Don't cry over . .
   ______________________________
4. When the cat's away, . . .
   ______________________________
5. Two heads . . .
   ______________________________
6. Two wrongs . . .
   ______________________________
7. Birds of a feather . . .
   ______________________________
8. The grass is always greener . . .
   ______________________________
9. Look before . . .
   ______________________________
10. Haste makes . . .
    ______________________________

# ANALOGIES

Analogies are comparisons. Complete each analogy below. An example has been done for you.

**Nephew is to uncle as niece is to aunt.**

1. ______________________ is to wings as fish is to fins.
2. Tennis is to ______________________ as baseball is to bat.
3. Jim is to James as Betsy is to ______________________.
4. Author is to story as poet is to ______________________.
5. Wide is to narrow as ______________________ is to short.
6. Lincoln is to ______________________ as Roosevelt is to Theodore.
7. ______________________ is to shell as pea is to pod.
8. Hard is to ______________________ as big is to small.
9. Dirt is to forest as ______________________ is to desert.
10. Frame is to picture as curtain is to ______________________.
11. Sing is to song as ______________________ is to book.
12. Braces are to ______________________ as contact lenses are to eyes.

7\. ______________________ is to flake as rain is to drop.

14. Scissors is to ______________________ as pen is to write.
15. Hat is to head as ______________________ is to foot.
16. Hammer is to nail as screwdriver is to ______________________.
17. Scarf is to neck as ______________________ is to finger.
18. Fingers are to ______________________ as toes are to feet.
19. ______________________ is to pig as neigh is to horse.
20. Second is to ______________________ as day is to week.

 

# WHICH WORD?

Words that sound alike or look alike often have meanings that are not alike. Decide which word is the correct one for each clue below and circle it.

| | |
|---|---|
| 1. Dry land | dessert/desert |
| 2. Complete | through/thorough |
| 3. Also | too/two/to |
| 4. Completely prepared | all ready/already |
| 5. To go forward | proceed/precede |
| 6. Writing paper | stationary/stationery |
| 7. Second in a series of two | latter/later |
| 8. A basic law | principle/principal |
| 9. Hush | quite/quiet |
| 10. Contraction for it is | its/it's |
| 11. To recline | lie/lay |
| 12. The result of a cause | affect/effect |
| 13. A part of speech | preposition/proposition |
| 14. In any case | any way/anyway |
| 15. To rest the body on something | sit/set |

# SIMILES

A simile is a figure of speech in which two unlike things are compared using the words *like* or *as*, such as in "he moved as quick as a wink." Complete the following common similes.

1. As fresh as ______________________
2. As white as ______________________
3. As wise as ______________________
4. As strong as ______________________
5. As flat as ______________________
6. As cold as ______________________
7. As hard as ______________________
8. As stubborn as ______________________
9. As cute as ______________________
10. As black as ______________________
11. As blind as ______________________
12. As happy as ______________________
13. As cool as ______________________
14. As stiff as ______________________
15. As clean as ______________________
16. As limp as ______________________
17. As busy as ______________________
18. As light as ______________________
19. As good as ______________________
20. As pretty as ______________________

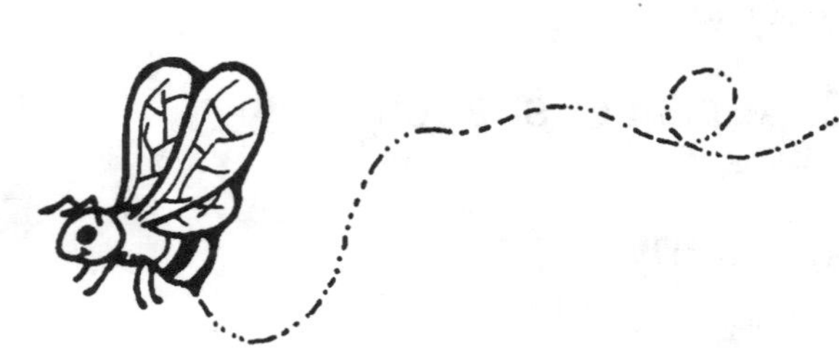

 

# COUNTRY AND CITY MATCH

Match the cities to their countries.

| | |
|---|---|
| Chicago | Canada |
| Paris | United States |
| Tokyo | England |
| Buenos Aires | Australia |
| Lima | Germany |
| Johannesburg | Russia |
| Marakesh | France |
| Rome | Mexico |
| Quebec | Sweden |
| Lagos | Morocco |
| Hanoi | South Africa |
| Sydney | Peru |
| Christchurch | China |
| Moscow | India |
| Peking | New Zealand |
| London | Japan |
| Stockholm | Argentina |
| Berlin | Italy |
| New Delhi | Vietnam |
| Guadalajara | Nigeria |

# ANSWER KEY

**Page 3**

1. Fred
2. Orville
3. Wally
4. Hobbes
5. Dale Evans
6. Jerry
7. Amos
8. Mutt
9. Beauty
10. Jane
11. Lucy
12. Bullwinkle
13. Laurel
14. Donald Duck
15. Tarzan

**Page 4**
Answers will vary.

**Page 5**
Answers will vary.

**Page 6**
Answers will vary.

**Page 7**
Some answers may vary.

1. dwarfs
2. sports
3. flowers
4. members of the cat family
5. desserts
6. tools
7. feelings
8. make-believe characters
9. products from a cow
10. mean "one"
11. round
12. transportation
13. vegetables
14. candy bars
15. girls' names beginning with C

**Page 8**

1. puff
2. feather
3. order
4. soul
5. cranny
6. match
7. lace
8. dogs
9. sugar
10. blue (or white)
11. quiet
12. holler (or shout)
13. forth (or front)
14. thin
15. nails
16. stones
17. learn (or let live)
18. tomato
19. nails
20. proper
21. dandy
22. cents
23. cream
24. shine

**Page 9**

1. green; primary colors
2. December; months with 30 days
3. calculus; types of clouds
4. cabbage; underground vegetables
5. shovel; have prongs
6. Susan; girls' names beginning with C
7. tomato; flowers
8. candy bar; baked goods
9. niece; males
10. Canada; continents
11. Cowboys; baseball teams or Dodgers; teams beginning with "C"
12. watermelon; citrus fruits
13. cry; about happiness
14. pig; poultry
15. east; intermediate directions

**Page 10**
Bess May is 10.
Liz Smith is 8.
Beth Jones is 9.

**Page 11**
David jogs for 15 minutes.
Tom bikes for 30 minutes.
Rick golfs for 45 minutes.
Roger swims for 60 minutes.

**Page 12**
Katelyn likes the roller coaster and ate bratwurst.
Kenny likes the ferris wheel and ate a hot dog.
Emily likes the bumper cars and ate a hamburger.
Howie likes the carousel and ate a corndog.

**Page 13**
Sarah: May 1
Jill: January 1
Millie: April 1
Andrew: February 12
Max: August 25
Jeff: October 9
Andrea: July 14
Maeve: March 10

**Page 14**
Chad: Reds
Danny: Cardinals
Andrew: White Sox
Ryan: Dodgers
Will: A's

**Page 15**

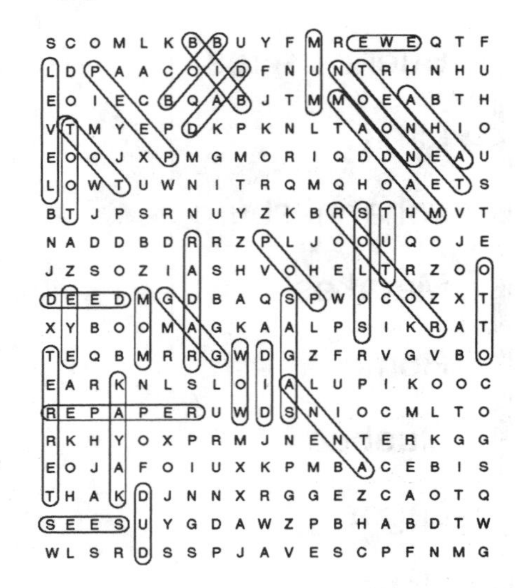

**Page 16**

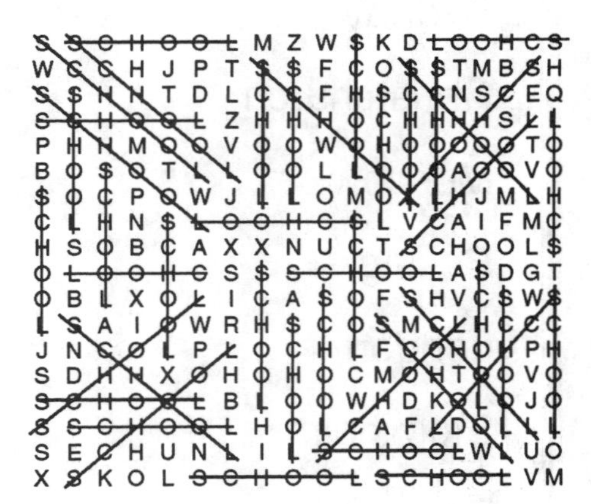

 

# ANSWER KEY (CONT.)

**Page 19**

1. tears
2. wise
3. night
4. children
5. charity or love
6. 'rithmetic
7. sinker
8. win
9. handsome
10. Larry
11. milk
12. stars
13. Nod
14. moe
15. hail

**Page 20**

1. skating on thin ice
2. right in the middle of everything
3. man in the moon
4. check up
5. crossroads
6. mind over matter
7. I am beside myself
8. bottoms up
9. beneath the sea
10. hand in hand
11. uptown
12. H2O (H to O)

**Page 21**

1. reading between the lines
2. half an hour
3. just between you and me
4. smallpox
5. man on the moon
6. worn out
7. long overdue
8. loosen up
9. turkey in the straw
10. going around in circles
11. Quit following me
12. Minnesota

**Page 23**

1. clock
2. cup
3. cupboard
4. dish
5. frying pan
6. candlestick
7. tub
8. mirror
9. bowl
10. range
11. light (or plate)
12. iron
13. closet

**Page 24**

1. EZ
2. IC
3. CU
4. P
5. C
6. K or D
7. O
8. I
9. I
10. TP
11. IV
12. Y
13. T
14. B
15. DJ

**Page 25**

1. blue
2. listen
3. stars
4. arithmetic
5. go
6. green or blue
7. win
8. roll
9. handsome
10. hail
11. Curly
12. milk
13. mineral
14. charity
15. moe

**Page 27**

1. + - - + +
2. + - + - +
3. - + - + +
4. - + + + -
5. - + + - +
6. - + + - +
7. + + - + +
8. + + - + -
9. - + + - -
10. + - + - -

**Page 28**

1. quarts in a gallon
2. years in a century
3. sides of a hexagon
4. inches in a yard
5. ounces in a pound
6. keys on a piano
7. minutes in an hour
8. days in a leap year
9. teaspoons in a tablespoon
10. cards in a deck
11. bones in your body
12. squares on a checkerboard
13. states in the U.S.
14. items in a baker's dozen
15. pounds in a ton
16. sun in our solar system
17. lakes in the Great Lakes
18. voices in a quintet
19. players on a baseball team
20. millimeters in a centimeter

**Page 29**

1. aviator
2. prophet
3. authors
4. senator
5. peanuts
6. flights
7. candies
8. pianist
9. Dodgers
10. New Deal
11. braille
12. soldier
13. painter
14. skating
15. general

**Page 30**

Answers will vary.

**Page 31**

Answers will vary.

**Page 32**

1. 1 silver dollar
2. 3q, 2d, 1n
3. 2q, 5d
4. 10d
5. 5d, 10n
6. 2q, 4d, 10p
7. 7d, 5n, 5p
8. 9d, 10p
9. 1q, 3d, 6n, 15p
10. 3q, 25p

**Page 33**

1. a graph
2. 90°
3. a time zone
4. 100
5. octagon
6. 10
7. 120
8. 21
9. no
10. 10
11. 6
12. length x width
13. 606
14. 70
15. 360°

**Page 34**

1. autobiography
2. *Little Women*
3. Aesop
4. Beatrix Potter
5. an author
6. adverb
7. Samuel Clemens
8. a period
9. palindromes
10. Fudge
11. proper nouns
12. quotation marks
13. fairy tales
14. a colon
15. four

**Page 35**

1. a microscope
2. Jupiter
3. muscles
4. a diamond
5. a barometer
6. the Earth
7. 98.6°F
8. orbit
9. Neptune until 1999
10. ribs
11. a galaxy
12. the iris
13. fossils
14. deciduous
15. the heartbeat

**Page 36**

1. Juneau
2. a peninsula
3. 6
4. John Wilkes Booth
5. Amerigo Vespucci
6. Lake Michigan
7. copper
8. Benjamin Franklin
9. west
10. France
11. Philadelphia
12. Hawaii and Alaska
13. Thomas Jefferson
14. Statue of Liberty
15. Betsy Ross

**Page 37**

1. escalator
2. every 4 years

# ANSWER KEY (CONT.)

**Page 37**

1. escalator
2. every 4 years
3. "Once upon a time"
4. quintuplets
5. a tripod
6. stamps
7. break it open to get the treats
8. black
9. a pride
10. the port
11. a stovepipe
12. a genie
13. a moat
14. the eye
15. a rabbit

**Page 38**

1. true
2. false
3. true
4. false
5. false
6. true
7. false
8. false
9. true
10. false
11. true
12. true
13. true
14. false
15. false

**Page 39**

1. 12
2. 66
3. 24 or 25
4. 103
5. 132
6. 13
7. 5
8. 4
9. 206
10. 32
11. 88
12. 144
13. 13
14. 100
15. 1

**Page 40**

1. bony pony
2. glum chum
3. slick chick
4. legal beagle
5. roast toast
6. grape ape
7. sad dad
8. funny bunny
9. Swiss miss
10. bug hug
11. rude dude
12. fender bender
13. pooch smooch
14. fat cat
15. darling starling
16. shy guy
17. mouse house
18. big pig
19. glad lad
20. lazy daisy

**Page 41**

1. President
2. as soon as possible
3. adjective
4. pounds
5. maximum
6. et cetera
7. September
8. Master of Arts
9. I owe you
10. Before Christ
11. collect on delivery
12. respondez sil vous plait (please reply)
13. self-addressed stamped envelope
14. South America
15. building
16. railroad
17. preposition
18. headquarters
19. District Attorney
20. Daylight Saving Time

**Page 42**

Answers will vary.

**Page 43**

Answers will vary.

**Page 44**

1. cold
2. colt
3. bolt
4. bold
5. bald
6. ball
7. bell
8. belt
9. melt
10. molt
11. mold
12. mole
13. hole
14. hold
15. gold
16. fold
17. food
18. fool
19. tool
20. pool

**Page 45**

1. grew
2. ewe
3. weed
4. edible
5. letter
6. erase
7. season
8. once
9. celebrate
10. telegram
11. amoré
12. read
13. admit
14. itch
15. chicken
16. entertain

**Page 46**

1. ten
2. net
3. tale
4. each
5. hare
6. Earth
7. hold
8. daily
9. yes
10. swim
11. mail
12. love
13. ear or eye

**Page 47**

1. barbecue
2. barrack
3. barbells
4. barbarian
5. barn
6. barberry
7. (Clara) Barton
8. bargain
9. baritone
10. baroness
11. Barbie
12. barge
13. barracuda
14. bareback
15. Barcelona

**Page 48**

1. bicentennial
2. price
3. slice
4. mice
5. iceberg
6. licorice
7. spice
8. Iceland
9. rice
10. triceratops
11. vice-president or vice-chancellor
12. *Alice in Wonderland*
13. advice
14. office
15. juice
16. biceps
17. device
18. entice
19. police
20. dice
21. choice
22. notice
23. thrice
24. lice
25. *The Price Is Right*

**Page 49**

1. *Goldfinger*
2. goldfish
3. goldbrick
4. Gold Coast
5. Goldilocks
6. gold digger
7. gold dust
8. golden
9. goldeneye
10. Golden Rule
11. gold mine
12. Gold Rush
13. golden anniversary
14. gold reserve
15. goldenrod
16. goldsmith
17. goldfinch

**Page 50**

1. green thumb
2. Tom Thumb
3. thumbs-up
4. Thumbelina
5. thumbprint
6. thumb a ride
7. thumbs down
8. thumb through
9. thumbtack
10. rule of thumb

# ANSWER KEY (CONT.)

11. all thumbs
12. under someone's thumb
13. thumb one's nose

**Page 51**

1. goat, goose, or gopher
2. golf
3. gondola
4. gold
5. gone
6. Golden Rule
7. golden retriever
8. goal
9. goober
10. go-between
11. gobble
12. goblin
13. gorgeous
14. gorilla
15. goulash
16. to get one's goat
17. goblet
18. goggles
19. *Gone With the Wind*
20. Goliath
21. gown
22. mango
23. tango
24. gourd
25. goldfinch

**Page 52**

1. cat
2. frog
3. goat
4. kid
5. dog
6. bear
7. camel
8. oyster
9. deer
10. gnu and owl
11. hen
12. lion
13. fish
14. seal
15. ape

**Page 53**

1. aardvark
2. summer or fall
3. football or baseball
4. intelligence
5. doodle
6. buccaneer
7. butterfly
8. giraffe
9. beggar
10. moon
11. pepper
12. gaggle
13. wiggle
14. borrow
15. sorrow
16. sonnet
17. ballot
18. classic

**Page 54**

1. SOS
2. hor d'oeuvre
3. southpaw
4. great
5. ambidextrous
6. doggy bag
7. white elephant
8. ad lib
9. gobbledy gook
10. vice versa
11. thank you
12. á la mode
13. many
14. hocus-pocus
15. et cetera

**Page 55**
**U.S. States**

1. New Mexico
2. South Dakota
3. North Carolina
4. New Jersey
5. New Hampshire
6. Rhode Island
7. South Carolina
8. New York
9. West Virginia
10. North Dakota

**Inventors**

1. Franklin
2. Fulton
3. Eastman
4. Gutenberg
5. Marconi
6. Whitney
7. Howe
8. Bell
9. Edison
10. Goodyear

**Page 56**
**Math Terms**

1. addition
2. multiplication
3. product
4. division
5. equation
6. equivalent
7. diameter
8. area
9. probability
10. square root

**School Terms**

1. recess
2. maps
3. desks
4. almanac
5. books
6. ruler
7. compass
8. teacher
9. pencils
10. principal

**Page 57**

1. Casper, Melchior, and Balthasar
2. Swine who made houses from straw, sticks, and brick
3. Rodents who ran after the farmer's wife
4. Papa, Mama, and Baby bears
5. Mizaru, Mazaru, and Mikazaru
6. Readin', writin', and 'rithmetic
7. Curly, Mo, and Larry
8. Athos, Aramis, and Porthos
10. gold, frankincense, and myrrh
11. Huey, Dewey, and Louie
14. length, width, and height
15. The butcher, the baker, and the candlestick maker

**Page 58**
Answers will vary. Some possible answers are: dialogue, auctioned, housemaid, cautioned, reputation, equation, pneumonia, discourage, ultraviolet, and encouraging.

**Page 59**
Answers will vary.

**Page 60**
Answers will vary.

**Page 61**
Answers will vary.
Many answers will be difficult to find, and some will be impossible.

**Page 62**
Answers will vary.

**Page 63**
Answers will vary.

**Page 64**
Answers will vary.

**Page 65**
An apple a day keeps the doctor away.

1. L
2. Y
3. D
4. W
5. T
6. F
7. R
8. A
9. E
10. S
11. N
12. K
13. O
14. H
15. C

**Page 66**

1. amnesia
2. hearth
3. eagle
4. kayak
5. Alberta
6. maximum
7. Europe, Australia or Asia
8. greeting
9. recover
10. nitrogen
11. wallow
12. doubled
13. erase
14. neon

**Page 67**
schoolroom
anyone
afternoon
backbone
blackboard
newspaper
homemade
bedtime
everyday
grandfather
elsewhere
cowboy
snowball
whoever

# ANSWER KEY (CONT.)

seashore
headline
railroad
outdoors
southeast
understand

**Page 68**

Answers will vary.

**Page 69**

1. A
2. S
3. A
4. H
5. S
6. H
7. H
8. S
9. A
10. S
11. H
12. A
13. S
14. H
15. H
16. A
17. S
18. H
19. S
20. A

**Page 70**

1. Bob, Otto
2. did
3. civic
4. noon
5. nun
6. ewe
7. mum
8. peep
9. Tut
10. kayak
11. tot
12. Anna, Hannah
13. level
14. gag
15. solos

**Page 71**

1. . . . what you can do today.
2. . . . is a friend indeed.
3. . . . spilled milk.
4. . . . the mice will play.
5. . . . are better than one.
6. . . . don't make a right.
7. . . . flock together.
8. . . . on the other side.
9. . . . you leap.
10. . . . waste.

**Page 72**

1. Bird
2. racket
3. Elizabeth
4. poem
5. tall (or long)
6. Abraham
7. Nut
8. soft
9. sand
10. window
11. read
12. teeth
13. Snow
14. cut
15. shoe
16. screw
17. ring
18. hands
19. Oink
20. minute

**Page 73**

1. desert
2. thorough
3. too
4. all ready
5. proceed
6. stationery
7. latter
8. principle
9. quiet
10. it's
11. lie
12. effect
13. preposition
14. anyway
15. sit

**Page 74**

1. a daisy
2. snow
3. an owl
4. an ox
5. a pancake
6. ice
7. nails
8. a mule
9. a button
10. coal
11. a bat
12. a lark
13. a cucumber
14. a board
15. a whistle
16. a wet noodle
17. a bee
18. a feather
19. gold
20. a picture

**Page 75**

Chicago, United States
Paris, France
Tokyo, Japan
Buenos Aires, Argentina
Lima, Peru
Johannesburg, South Africa
Marrakech, Morocco
Rome, Italy
Quebec, Canada
Lagos, Nigeria
Hanoi, Vietnam
Sydney, Australia
Christchurch, New Zealand
Moscow, Russia
Peking, China
London, England
Stockholm, Sweden
Berlin, Germany
New Delhi, India
Guadalajara, Mexico